Specials!

Britain in the 20th century

Steve Waugh

Acknowledgements

© 2006 Folens Limited, on behalf of the author.

United Kingdom: Folens Publishers, Apex Business Centre, Boscombe Road, Dunstable, LU5 4RL.
Email: folens@folens.com

Ireland: Folens Publishers, Greenhills Road, Tallaght, Dublin 24.
Email: info@folens.ie

Poland: JUKA, ul. Renesansowa 38, Warsaw 01-905.

Editor: Janice Baiton   Layout artist: Book Matrix, India   Illustrations: Tony Randell
Cover design: Corbis   Cover image: Mary Evans Picture Library

First published 2006 by Folens Limited.

Every effort has been made to contact copyright holders of material used in this publication. If any copyright holder has been overlooked, we should be pleased to make any necessary arrangements.

British Library Cataloguing in Publication Data. A catalogue record for this publication is available from the British Library.

ISBN 1-84303-983-4

Contents

Introduction

Specials! History have been specifically written for teachers to use with students who may struggle with some of the skills and concepts needed for Key Stage 3 History. The titles are part of a wider series from Folens for use with lower ability students.

Each book in the series contains ten separate units covering the topics needed to complete the theme of the book. Each unit has one or more photocopiable resource sheets and several activity sheets. This allows the teacher to work in different ways. The tasks are differentiated throughout the book and offer all students the opportunity to expand their skills. Hopefully, by using photocopiable writing frames and emphasising literacy skills, students will be able to access historical information more easily.

The teacher's page at the start of each unit gives guidance on the material and is laid out as follows.

Objectives
These are the main skills or knowledge to be learned.

Prior knowledge
This refers to the minimum skills or knowledge required by students to complete the tasks. As a rule, students should have a reading comprehension age of 6 to 9 years and should be working at levels 1 to 3. Some activity sheets are more challenging than others and teachers will need to select accordingly.

QCA and NC links; Scottish attainment targets
All units link to the QCA scheme of work and to the NC for History at Key Stage 3. There are also links to the Scottish 5–14 guidelines.

Background
This provides additional information for the teacher, expanding on historical details or giving further information about the unit.

Starter activity
Since the units can be taught as a lesson, a warm-up activity focusing on an aspect of the unit is suggested.

Resource sheets and activity sheets
The resource sheets, which are often visual but may also be written, do not include tasks and can be used as stimulus for discussion. Related tasks are provided on the activity sheets.

Where necessary, keywords are included on the student pages. Other keywords are included on the teacher's page. These can be introduced to students at the teacher's discretion and depending on students' abilities

Assessment sheet
At the end of each unit is an assessment sheet focusing on student progress. It can be used in different ways. A student can complete it as a self-assessment, while the teacher also completes one on each student's progress. They can then compare the two. This is useful in situations where the teacher or classroom assistant is working with one student. Alternatively, students can work in pairs to carry out peer assessments and then compare the outcomes with each other. Starting from a simple base that students can manage, the assessment sheet allows the student to discuss their own progress, to consider different points of view and to discuss how they might improve, thus enabling the teacher to see the work from the student's perspective.

Plenary
The teacher can use the suggestions here to recap on the main points covered or to reinforce a particular idea.

Look out for other titles in the History series, which include:
- The Romans
- Medieval Britain 1066–1485
- Changing Britain 1485–1750
- Industrial Britain 1750–1900

Teacher's notes

Slavery and the slave trade

Objectives

- Understand slave trade and slavery and arguments for and against this
- Annotate maps
- Select and organise arguments
- Empathise with slaves

Prior knowledge

Students should have some understanding of the difference between slavery and freedom and the key continents involved.

QCA link

Unit 15 Black peoples of America: from slavery to equality?

NC links

History skills 2a, 2b, 2c, 4a, 4b, 5a and 5c

Scottish attainment targets

Environmental Studies – Society – People in the past
Strand – People, events and societies of significance in the past
Level D
Level E

Background

Slavery was not new to the eighteenth century. Indeed, it dates back to the Romans and before. The first Europeans to take part in the slave trade were the Portuguese and the Spanish in the fifteenth century. They transported slaves from Africa to their colonies in the Americas. By 1570, there were about 20 000 slaves in Mexico alone. As other countries saw how much profit was to be made, they were quick to claim land in the Americas and bring across slaves. In 1619, the first black slave arrived in a British colony.

Starter activity

Students need to understand the key difference between slavery and freedom. Brainstorm key features of each. Ask the students to produce two mind maps: one showing main features of freedom and the other showing key features of slavery.

Resource sheets and activity sheets

Students should research the slave trade using 'The slave trade' and find out the meaning of the triangular trade and the middle passage. The middle passage could be done as a whole-class activity to highlight the terrible conditions on the journey.

For 'Arrival in America', ask the students to devise a role play showing the 'scramble'.

For 'Slavery', divide the class into groups, each of which researches and gives feedback to the whole class on the daily routine, the treatment of slaves, the arguments for abolition of slavery and the arguments against it.

For 'Mapping the slave trade' students need a clear understanding of the triangular trade. Ask the students to perform a role play in which each part of the triangle is acted out. Obtain feedback from the students on why people supported slavery.

For 'The campaign against the slave trade', the students should make use of the various sources about the middle passage. Encourage students to read out extracts from their diary as well as their final letter to William Wilberforce.

For 'Slavery in America', students need to categorise the statements. Again, encourage students to give feedback on what they think is the strongest argument for and against. Encourage diverse choices.

Assessment sheet

Students should complete this sheet to evaluate their overall understanding of slavery and the slave trade and of the key skills developed.

Plenary

Students should imagine that a slave from the late eighteenth century who experienced the middle passage and life in the America is visiting the class for a question-and-answer session. In pairs, they decide on three questions they would like to ask the slave. Get feedback from each pair and decide on the three most popular questions. Students, again in pairs, should work out how the slave might have answered the questions.

The slave trade

During the eighteenth century, the slave trade grew and a triangular trade was established. Cheap labour was needed in the cotton plantations of the United States and the sugar plantations of the West Indies.

The triangular trade

Slave ships sailed from Europe to the west coast of Africa. The ships were packed with goods, such as trinkets, guns, metal and cotton supplies. These goods were exchanged for slaves provided by the local chiefs. The ships, packed with slaves, then sailed across the Atlantic to America and the West Indies. Here, with their profits, the merchants bought cargoes of sugar, rum, tobacco or cotton and sailed back across the Atlantic to Europe for more profit.

The middle passage

This was the name given to the journey from Africa to America or the West Indies. The ships were fitted out to take as many slaves as possible on the journey. Men and women were separated. The men were chained by the ankle in pairs. There was not enough room in the hold to stand up. Overcrowding and filth meant that disease spread quickly. Many died and some jumped overboard. The journey took between five and eight weeks.

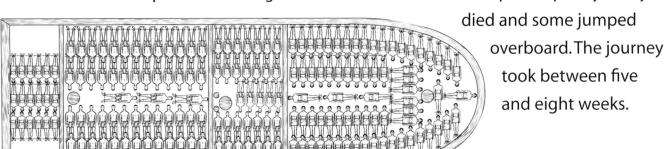

Source A   A plan of slaves crammed into one deck on a slave ship

She had taken 336 males and 226 females. The space between the decks was so low that they sat between each other's legs, so close that there was no possibility of their lying down or changing their positions day or night. The thermometer was standing at 32 degrees Celsius.

Source B   Captain Newton's description of conditions on board his slave ship

Specials! History Britain in the 20th century

Arrival in America

Those that survived the middle passage were cleaned up before they arrived in America. Oil was rubbed on their skin to make them look healthy and to hide any signs of sickness. Healthy and fit slaves brought more profit. The slaves were sold directly to planters or to middle men who would sell them. Some were sold by public auction (see Source C), while others were sold in a scramble (see Source D).

Source C   A slave auction in Virginia, USA   ▶

On a signal, given by the beat of a drum, the buyers rushed into the yard where the slaves were confined like sheep in a pen, and chose the ones they liked best. The noise and clamour, and the eagerness shown on the faces of the buyers, increased the fear of the terrified Africans.

Source D   A slave describes the 'scramble'

Husbands and wives, parents and children were separated forever as potential buyers inspected them as if they were animals in a market. Once bought, they were branded with a number or mark on their skin so people could see who owned them. Most were then taken to farms or plantations and set to work in the fields.

Arguments against slavery

A campaign against the slave trade developed in Britain in the late eighteenth century. It was led by an MP called William Wilberforce. Here are some of the arguments used against the trade.

- Slavery itself was wrong – one person could not own another.
- The slaves were being forcibly taken from their homes in West Africa.
- Families were split up.
- Many slaves died during the middle passage because of the terrible conditions.

Slavery

The work of the slaves

The slaves often lived in huts that were some distance from the plantation house. They started work at 6:00am and were divided into three 'gangs'. The first gang was made up of the fittest young men and women. They did the hardest work. The youngest and oldest and those who had been disabled by accidents made up the second gang. The weakest of all made up the third gang who did very light work.

They worked until 6:00pm, with a break for breakfast at 9:00am and a two-hour break in the middle of the day. Women worked in the fields and also as house slaves.

The treatment of slaves

After arriving on the plantation, the life expectancy of a slave was about eight years. They did not live long because:

- diseases such as yellow fever, leprosy, dysentery and tuberculosis were common;
- punishments were harsh, including regular beatings. One female slave had her ear nailed to a tree for breaking a plate.

Source E   A slave being whipped by another slave   ▶

None of the evils of slavery are more horrible than the treatment of females. They were obliged to give in to prostitution, to do equal labour with males and to become the breeders of slaves at the will and pleasure of their masters.

Source F   From Major J.B. Colthurst, a special judge who was sent to the Caribbean to investigate slavery in 1847

Arguments against slavery

Gradually, a strong movement developed in the northern states of the USA against slavery. In 1832, the Anti-Slavery Society was set up.

Mapping the slave trade

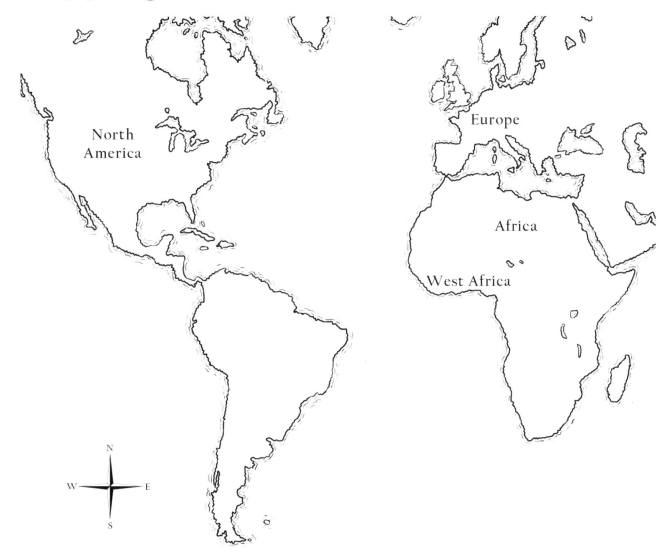

☞ On the map above do the following.

- Draw a triangle to show the triangular trade. Your triangle should link Europe, West Africa and North America.
- Write on your triangle what would be taken on each part of the trade.

☞ Why did people in Britain support slavery and the slave trade? Choose from the following reasons and write them on the map.

- It benefitted the black Africans who were transported to America.
- Merchants made big profits from the trade in slaves.
- It provided cheap labour for the sugar and cotton plantations in America and the West Indies.
- It took the slaves to a better life.

The campaign against the slave trade

It is 1790. You are a friend of William Wilberforce who is campaigning in Britain against slavery and the slave trade and you are going to collect evidence against the slave trade. You agree to work on board a slave ship on the middle passage from Africa to America.

☞ Keep a diary of what you witness.

- Use the evidence on the resource sheets and give yourself a name.
- On a separate sheet of paper, write extracts from your diary for days 1, 14, 21, 30 and 64. You should include getting the slaves in West Africa, conditions on board, the journey, what happened to the slaves on reaching America. The first entry has been started for you.

The Diary of

_____

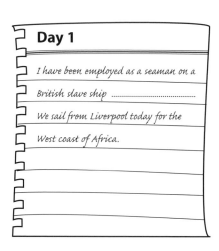

Day 1

I have been employed as a seaman on a
British slave ship ....
We sail from Liverpool today for the
West coast of Africa.

☞ On a separate sheet of paper, copy and complete the letter below to Wilberforce. Use the evidence from your diary to give reasons why the slave trade should be abolished.

Dear William

I have worked as a seamen on board the_____and have witnessed the slave trade including taking the slaves in Africa, the journey from Africa to America and the selling of the slaves in America. As a result of this, I believe the slave trade should be abolished.

My first reason is…	This is because…
My second reason is…	This is because…
My third reason is…	This is because…

Slavery in America

By the mid-nineteenth century, the USA was divided into those who supported slavery, mainly in the southern states, and those who opposed slavery, mainly in the northern states. This was one of the events that eventually led to a civil war.

☞ Read the statements below. Then, on a separate sheet of paper, copy the table below and complete it by writing each statement under the heading you think is best.

- Black people were equal in the eyes of God.
- The economy of the southern states would collapse without slave labour.
- America was supposed to be a free country. It was against the US constitution to have slavery.
- Slaves were happy to work. They had all they needed and did not know how to look after themselves.
- What would the slaves do if it was not for the slave plantations?
- Black people could be sent back to Africa to live freely.
- Slaves were treated like animals and often beaten.
- Black people could not think for themselves and needed to be told what to do.
- Slaves were separated from the rest of their family.
- Black people had fought against the British in the American War of Independence (1775–83) and deserved their freedom.
- Slaves were needed to work new machines called cotton gins.

Arguments for	Arguments against

☞ Which do you think was the most convincing argument on either side?

_____

Why?

_____

Assessment sheet – Slavery and the slave trade

✓ Tick the boxes to show what you know.

I know:	Yes	Not sure	Don't know
what is meant by the triangular trade			
what is meant by the middle passage			
why many slaves died during the middle passage			
who William Wilberforce was			
why many people opposed the slave trade			
why many people opposed slavery			
how to annotate a map			
how to make diary entries			

I know best: _____

I need to work on (up to three targets):

–

–

–

Teacher's notes

Black Americans after emancipation, 1865–1945

Objectives

- Understand chronology of key events
- Make judgements on impact of change

Prior knowledge

Students should have some understanding of slavery and the emancipation of slaves in the USA.

QCA link

Unit 15 Black peoples of America: from slavery to equality?

NC links

History skills 1, 2c, 5a, 5b and 5c

Scottish attainment targets

Environmental Studies – Society – People in the past
Strand – Time and historical sequence
Level C
Strand – Change, continuity, cause and effect
Level D

Background

The US Civil War was fought for a variety of reasons with the abolition of slavery being a key factor. The defeat of the South resulted in the end of slavery and the emancipation of the slaves.

Starter activity

Show students the illustration of the Ku Klux Klan on 'Black Americans after emancipation'. Encourage them to ask questions, such as What is happening? Why are they dressed this way? Explain briefly about the KKK. What does it suggest about black Americans after emancipation?

Resource sheets and activity sheets

Students should be divided into groups and each given one key development on 'Black Americans after emancipation' and 'What happened after emancipation?' to research. Students should give feedback on each event.

For 'Changes to black Americans (1)', students should organise the events chronologically and summarise each event. Explain the colour coding, judgement on change and key. Stress that these judgements are subjective – there is no right or wrong answer. Possibly do the first as a whole-class activity.

For 'Changes to black Americans (2)', the students should plot the key developments on the graph and then write down the trends. Obtain feedback on their trends and their views on black Americans after emancipation.

Assessment sheet

Students should complete this sheet to evaluate their overall understanding of black Americans after emancipation and of the key skills developed.

Plenary

In pairs, the students should imagine that they are leaders of black Americans after the Second World War. What would their aims be? Ask them to write down three or four aims and obtain feedback from each pair on these.

Black Americans after emancipation

Freedom?

At the end of the American Civil War (1861–65), the slaves were emancipated (given their freedom). How free were these black Americans? Did they achieve civil rights?

The Ku Klux Klan

The Ku Klux Klan became really popular in the 1920s with a membership of over five million. It was a secret society whose aim was to maintain white supremacy and terrorise non-white or non-Americans, especially black people. They often 'lynched' or executed black people by hanging them if they were suspected (but generally not proven) of committing a crime. Members of the KKK dressed in white robes and hoods so that they could not be recognised.

Source A A meeting of the Ku Klux Klan

The Second World War

From 1941 to 1945, there was some progress for black Americans.

- They were allowed to train as pilots.
- From 1944, black soldiers fought in integrated units with white soldiers.
- Fifty-eight black sailors had risen to the rank of officer.
- The government banned discrimination against black workers in industry.
- Many black people moved to the north and found jobs in industry.

However:

- There was little progress in civil rights in the South, where segregation continued.
- Very few black members of the armed forces became officers.

The First World War

From 1917 to 1918, many black soldiers fought as part of the US army in Europe and died for their country. However, they fought in blacks-only units, segregated from whites with white-only commanders.

What happened after emancipation?

Sharecropping

Most freed slaves went back to work for their original masters. Sharecropping was brought in immediately after 1865. Plantation owners could not afford to pay their workers until their crops had been harvested. Therefore a system was set up which allowed black people to work the land and keep a third of the crops as their wages. This meant they relied on good harvests and the plantation owners. It was not very different from slavery.

Marcus Garvey

Marcus Garvey was from Jamaica. In 1916, he moved to the USA where he set up the Universal Negro Improvement Association. This encouraged:

- black people to be proud of their race and African roots.
- black people to move from the USA to an African country called Liberia.

The Jim Crow Laws

Between 1890 and 1910, many Southern states greatly reduced the rights of black people through a series of laws known as the Jim Crow Laws.

- Black people were segregated. This meant they were forced to use separate hotels, transport, churches, theatres, schools and hospitals.

- Black people were discriminated against, especially in housing, education and employment. In other words, white children, workers or families got first choice in everything.

Source B A segregated 'White only' launderette in the American South ▶

The Freedmen's Bureau

This was set up in 1865 to help the freed slaves. It tried to improve their basic education, especially literacy. This was because in many southern states, black people had to be able to read and write to be registered as a voter. By 1874, the Bureau had increased literacy among black people. However, most southern states ignored the Bureau.

Changes to black Americans (1)

☞ Resource sheets 'Black Americans after emancipation' and 'What happened after emancipation?' give the main developments in civil rights for black Americans for the years 1865 to 1945. However, someone has jumbled up the events. You should:

- put the events in chronological order in the table below.
- write a brief explanation of each event.

Event number	Date	Explanation
1		
2		
3		
4		
5		
6		
7		

☞ Lightly shade each event on your table according to whether it greatly improved the position of black Americans, slightly improved, no change, slightly worsened or greatly worsened their position. Complete the key below with your colours.

Key

greatly improved   slightly improved   no change

slightly worsened   greatly worsened

Changes to black Americans (2)

☞ Create a graph by plotting your statements from the table on 'Changes to black Americans (1)' on the graph below. Use the statement numbers to do this. Once you have completed this, join up the numbers.

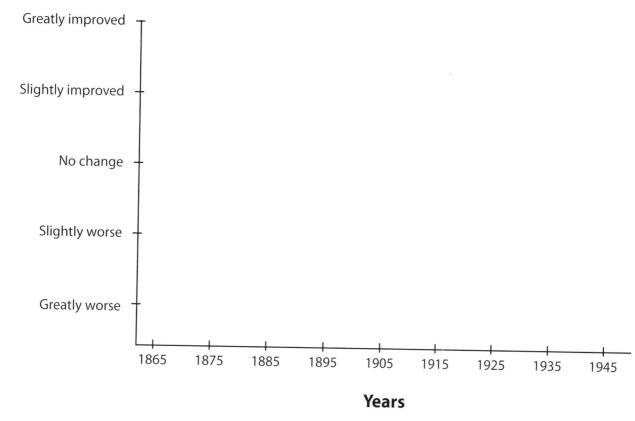

☞ What does the graph show? Write about two trends.

The first trend is _____

_____

The second trend is _____

_____

☞ Do you think the position of black Americans improved in the years 1865–1945?

Overall, I believe _____

This is because _____

_____

Assessment sheet – Black Americans after emancipation, 1865–1945

✓ Tick the boxes that show what you know.

I know:

	Yes	Not sure	Don't know
what is meant by the Ku Klux Klan			
how the two world wars helped black Americans			
what is meant by sharecropping			
how black Americans were helped by the work of the Freedmen's Bureau			
what Marcus Garvey did for black Americans			
what is meant by the Jim Crow Laws			
how to plot change on a graph			

I know best: _____

I need to work on (up to three targets):

— _____

— _____

— _____

Teacher's notes

The campaign for civil rights

Objectives

- Understand key features of the civil rights movement in the 1950s and 1960s
- Sequence key events
- Make judgements on methods used to campaign and key individuals

Prior knowledge

Students should have some understanding of the meaning of civil rights and the position of black Americans in the 1950s.

QCA link

Unit 15 Black peoples of America: from slavery to equality?

NC links

History skills 1, 2c, 2e, 5a and 5c

Scottish attainment targets

Environmental Studies – Society – People in the past
Strand – People, events and societies of significance in the past
Level D
Strand – Change, continuity, cause and effect
Level D

Background

Although black Americans made some progress during the Second World War, there was still widespread segregation and discrimination against them, especially in the southern states. They were still considered second-class citizens. The Supreme Court, the highest court in the USA, was increasingly targeted by civil rights campaigners as a method of improving civil rights.

Starter activity

Read Martin Luther King's 'I have a dream' speech on resource sheet 'Civil rights in the 1960s'. Ask the students why this was a dream. Students should be given two minutes to find out anything they can about King. The results could be written on sticky notes and placed round the classroom.

Resource sheets and activity sheets

For 'Civil rights in the 1950s', students should be divided into groups and asked to research either the Montgomery Bus Boycott or Little Rock. They should then prepare a role play exercise to show what happened and perform it to the rest of the class who should work out the key events/features.

For 'Civil rights in the 1960s', divide the students into four groups. Each group should research one of the four groups/leaders on the resource sheet and give feedback to the rest of the class with a summary of their methods and achievements.

For 'Key events of the 1950s', stress the need to use sketches and speech bubbles to complete the storyboard. For the Little Rock activity, emphasise that students can use text language but must get across the key events of the day that Little Rock students were escorted into school. Ask for volunteers to read out their texts.

For 'Different civil rights groups of the 1960s', encourage students to make judgements on the effectiveness of the methods used. Prompt this with a class discussion of the advantages/disadvantages of violent versus peaceful methods. Ask students to work in pairs and give feedback on their ratings. Emphasise the need to justify their ratings and finish with a class vote on the most effective leader/group.

Assessment sheet

Students should complete this sheet to evaluate their overall understanding of the campaign for civil rights and of the key skills developed.

Plenary

Students should think of one key word they have learnt on civil rights. Ask for volunteers to mime or draw their word for the rest of the class to guess.

Civil rights in the 1950s

During the 1950s, the campaign for civil rights for black Americans was stepped up and a new leader emerged, Martin Luther King.

The Montgomery Bus Boycott 1955

There was segregation on public transport in most of the southern states. Black Americans had to give up their seats to white people if the vehicle was becoming full. A black woman called Rosa Parks was asked by a bus driver in Montgomery to give up her seat to a white man. She refused and was arrested. A local minister of the church, Martin Luther King, took up her case and set up the Montgomery Improvement Association (MIA).

The MIA organised a boycott of the local bus company that lasted for 400 days. At the same time, the MIA made appeals to the highest court in the USA, the Supreme Court, to end segregation on public transport. In September 1956, the Court declared segregation was against the law and the boycott was called off.

Little Rock High School, 1957

Source A   Black American students being escorted into Little Rock High School ▶

The Supreme Court had made it illegal to segregate in schools. However, the Governor of Arkansas, Orval Faubus, was a racist who wanted black and white students educated separately. He refused to allow nine black students to attend a school in the town of Little Rock, and on 3 September 1957, blocked it with National Guardsmen. The following day they were removed and the students had to have a police escort into the school. The students were screamed at by a crowd of white people and, by midday, were sent home because their safety could not be guaranteed.

The president, Eisenhower, sent federal troops to protect the nine students for the rest of the school year. They still faced constant bullying from the white children.

Civil rights in the 1960s

The campaign for civil rights continued into the 1960s but it split into various groups, ranging from the peaceful methods of King to the violence of the Black Panthers.

Martin Luther King

Martin Luther King believed in non-violent protest. He believed black people should not retaliate against white racism or violence but show they deserved civil rights. His methods included:

- The Montgomery bus boycott.
- Massive marches to gain publicity. Two famous marches took place in 1963. The first was in Birmingham, Alabama, to protest against continued segregation. The second was in Washington, during which King made his famous 'I have a dream' speech.

'I have a dream that one day on the red hills of Georgia, the sons of former slaves and sons of former slave owners will be able to sit down together at the table of brotherhood.

I have a dream that my four little children will one day live in a nation where they will not be judged by the colour of their skin but by the content of their character.'

Black Power

Many young black Americans became frustrated by King's slow, peaceful methods. They were led by Stokely Carmichael and wanted blacks to have pride in their heritage. They used the slogan 'Black is Beautiful'. Black Power also encouraged more violent protest, especially riots.

Malcolm X

Some black Americans believed that King's peaceful methods were too slow. The most famous was Malcolm X, who had rejected his original slave name and replaced it with an 'X'. He had a great influence on young black Americans, arguing that violence had to be met with violence. He also rejected the idea of civil rights in the USA. Instead, he wanted a separate state for black Americans.

The Black Panthers

The Black Panthers were a violent group. They wore uniforms and were prepared to use weapons. They wanted to force white Americans to give them equal rights and clashed many times with the police. They killed nine police officers between 1967 and 1969.

Key events of the 1950s

The Montgomery Bus Boycott

☞ Below is a storyboard for the events of the Montgomery Bus Boycott of 1955 but some parts are missing. Complete the storyboard and add captions and speech bubbles where necessary.

Little Rock

☞ You witness the events at Little Rock High School in 1957. Imagine that mobile phones existed at that time. Text a friend describing what took place. On a separate sheet of paper, write your text and remember:

- you have 160 letters only
- you can use text language
- you need to get across the key events.

Different civil rights groups of the 1960s

☞ Which person/group do you think was the most successful in achieving civil rights for black Americans in the 1960s?

- Complete the grid below.
- Rate each group/leader out of 10 (10 = very successful, 0 = total failure).
- Give a brief explanation for your rating.

Leader/group	Methods used	Rating 1–10
Martin Luther King		
Malcolm X		
Black Power		
Black Panthers		

☞ Which person/group do you think achieved the most for civil rights in the 1960s?

Overall, I believe that _____

This is because _____

_____

Assessment sheet – The campaign for civil rights

✓ Tick the boxes that show what you know.

I know:

	Yes	Not sure	Don't know
what methods Martin Luther King used			
why the Montgomery Bus Boycott is important			
what happened at Little Rock High School in 1957			
what methods Malcolm X used			
who the Black Panthers were			
what is meant by the Black Power Movement			
how to use a storyboard			

I know best: _____

I need to work on (up to three targets):

–

–

–

Teacher's notes

Hot war: the First World War

Objectives

- Understand causation – long term, short term and immediate
- Sequence key events
- Make judgements on relative importance of factors

Prior knowledge

Students should have some understanding of causation and of Europe before the First World War.

QCA link

Unit 18 Hot war, cold war: why did the major twentieth-century conflicts affect so many people?

NC links

History skills 1, 2c, 2e, 5a, 5b and 5c

Scottish attainment targets

Environmental Studies – Society – People in the past
Strand – People, events and societies of significance in the past
Level E
Strand – Change, continuity, cause and effect
Level E

Background

The First World War was the result of rivalry between the Great Powers – France, Britain, Austria-Hungary, Russia and Germany. Students need to have an understanding of the map of Europe before 1914 and, more especially, the central powers and the Balkans.

Starter activity

Use an account or sketch of the assassination of Franz Ferdinand. In pairs, ask the students to think of one question about the assassination but to keep the question to themselves for the time being. Stress the importance of the assassination as the immediate cause of the First World War.

Resource sheets and activity sheets

For 'The causes of the First World War', students may need assistance to understand some of these reasons. A role play, with students taking on the guise of a country, could help them to grasp the importance of the alliance system and the arms race. Students could prepare their own role play on the assassination at Sarajevo together with the events that followed and led to full-scale war.

For 'Trench warfare', students should work in pairs and write down three or four reasons why there was stalemate on the Western Front. Obtain feedback from the class on these reasons.

Students may need initial help with 'Why did war break out in 1914?'. The first two reasons could be done as a whole-class activity. Ask students to plot the reasons and then discuss the relative importance of each reason as a whole class. What do they believe is the fundamental reason(s)?

For 'Western Front stalemate', complete one box together with the class. Obtain feedback from the students on the advice they would give to commanders.

Assessment sheet

Students should complete this sheet to evaluate their overall understanding of the First World War and of the key skills developed.

Plenary

Students should go back to their original question on the murder at Sarajevo. In pairs, they should try to answer this question. Ask for volunteers to give their original question and answer. Also pose the 'What if…?' question. What ideas have they come up with as commanders to end the stalemate? Discuss the various suggestions with the class. How realistic are they?

The causes of the First World War

In 1914, war broke out between the Great Powers. On the one side were Britain, France, Russia and Serbia and on the other were Germany and Austria-Hungary.

The assassination of Archduke Franz-Ferdinand, 28 June 1914

On 28 June 1914, the heir to the Austrian throne, Archduke Franz Ferdinand, and his wife, Sophie, were making an official visit to the capital of Bosnia, Sarajevo. They were both shot at close range by a Serbian terrorist called Gavrilo Princip and died. Austria, supported by Germany, declared war on Serbia. Serbia was supported by Russia, Britain and France.

Austro-Serbian rivalry

Austria and Serbia had been bitter rivals since the 1870s. Serbia wished to unite all Serbs into one country. This included Bosnia and some parts of the Austrian empire. Austria wished to crush Serbia.

Bosnian crisis 1908

In 1908, Austria took over Bosnia. This infuriated the Serbs who wanted Bosnia to become part of Serbia.

The arms race

There was a race between the Great Powers in the 25 years before 1914 as power increased the size of their armed forces and developed more destructive weapons. The bigger the armies, the more likely each country was to go to war.

The Alliance system

Between 1879 and 1907, the Great Powers became divided into two armed camps. The Triple Alliance was set up in 1882 and included Germany, Austria and Italy.

The Dreadnought

In 1906, Britain launched HMS *Dreadnought*, the most advanced warship in the world. This led to a race between Britain and Germany to build the most dreadnoughts.

Trench warfare

At the end of 1914, both sides dug trenches on the Western Front.

Stalemate

Over the next three and a half years, each side launched attacks known as offensives to try to break through the enemy trenches. They all failed, which meant a stalemate and very little movement. The main reasons for the stalemate were:

- The novelty of trench warfare. Neither side had faced such a defensive system.
- The lack of ideas from commanders on both sides. They believed that mass attacks would achieve a breakthrough. Generally, they just caused huge casualties.
- The strength of the trench system.
- The weather. The trenches suffered from frequent rainfall, which made it very difficult to attack quickly. Many offensives became bogged down in the mud.

The trench system

The trench system became stronger as the war developed. At first there was only one line of trenches, but by 1916 both sides had two or three lines. Each line of trenches was defended by barbed wire often several metres high and wide.

The trenches were defended by machine guns capable of firing 600 rounds a minute. These were well protected and ideal for breaking up enemy attacks. The area between the two armies was known as no-man's land. This was a deserted strip of land where all trees, buildings and cover had been destroyed. It was churned up by constant shelling.

Most trenches were deep enough for a man to walk without his head being seen and wide enough for a man to rest in. The soldiers lived in dugouts in the side walls of the trenches.

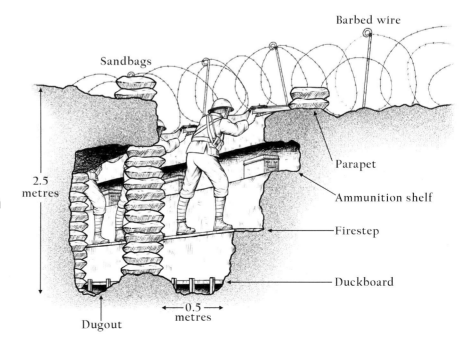

Why did war break out in 1914?

☞ On the road to war below, organise the causes of the First World War into the following categories:

- Long-term – more than ten years before the war broke out – on the first part.
- Short-term – less than ten years before the war broke out – on the middle part.
- Immediate – the final trigger.
- Shade the reasons in three colours:
  - ❏ most important red   ❏ quite important green   ❏ least important blue.

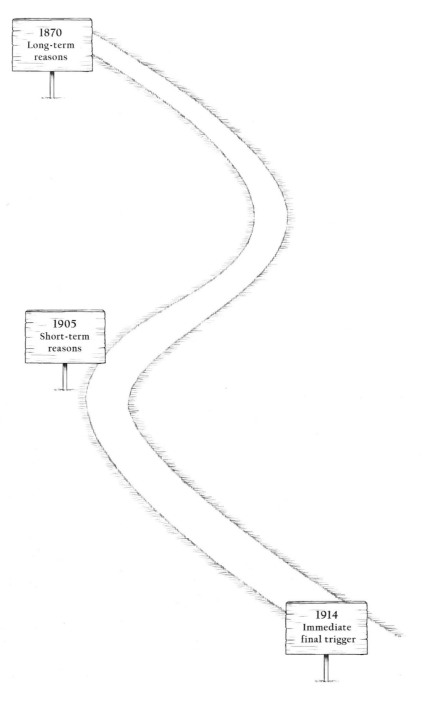

Western Front stalemate

During the First World War, most of the fighting in western Europe was trench warfare. Neither side was able to break through for over three years. This led to stalemate.

☞ On the diagram below, fill in the boxes with reasons for this stalemate.

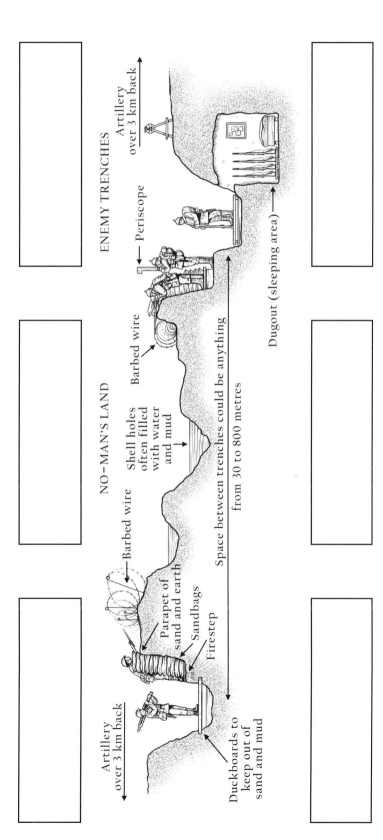

NO–MAN'S LAND

ENEMY TRENCHES

Artillery over 3 km back

Periscope

Barbed wire

Shell holes often filled with water and mud

Space between trenches could be anything from 30 to 800 metres

Dugout (sleeping area)

Barbed wire

Parapet of sand and earth

Sandbags

Firestep

Duckboards to keep out of sand and mud

Artillery over 3 km back

☞ You are a British commander on the Western Front in 1916. On a separate sheet of paper, copy and complete the writing frame below.

In order to break the stalemate I would use...   This would work because...

Another possibility would be...   This would work because...

Assessment sheet – Hot war: the First World War

✓ Tick the boxes to show what you know.

I know:	Yes	Not sure	Don't know
what is meant by a dreadnought			
why Austria and Serbia were rivals			
how the alliance system increased rivalry			
who was assassinated at Sarajevo in June 1914			
why there was a stalemate on the Western Front			
what is meant by no-man's land			
how to organise reasons into long term, short term and immediate			
how to use a writing grid			

I know best: _____

I need to work on (up to three targets):

—

—

—

Teacher's notes

The Cold War

Objectives

- Understand different interpretations of the Cold War
- Understand key events of the Cuban Missile Crisis

Prior knowledge

Students should have some understanding of the superpowers and the difference between communism and capitalism.

QCA link

Unit 18 Hot war, cold war: why did the major twentieth-century conflicts affect so many people?

NC links

History skills 3a, 3b, 5b and 5c

Scottish attainment targets

Environmental Studies – Society – People in the past
Strand – Change, continuity, cause and effect
Level D
Level E

Background

Students need an understanding of the background to the Cold War – the ideological differences between communism and capitalism as well as the East–West rivalry prior to the Second World War, such as western help for the Whites versus the Reds during the Russian Civil War of 1918–21. Stalin was suspicious of the West throughout the inter-war years and was convinced that they were encouraging a Nazi invasion – which indeed took place in 1941. The wartime alliance was a marriage of convenience – to defeat Nazism – and had begun to disintegrate towards the end of the war as Churchill warned the USA about Soviet expansionism in eastern Europe.

Starter activity

In pairs, ask the students to show the difference between a hot war and a cold war. They can use: a mini role play; an illustration or storyboard; or bullet points. Help them by explaining that the First World War was a hot war.

Resource sheets and activity sheets

For 'The reasons for the Cold War', the class should be divided into half – one half should read the Soviet and the other half the Western interpretation. Obtain feedback from the students on the differences between the two interpretations.

For 'The Cuban Missile Crisis', students should read the key events and decide on which dates there was the greatest threat of nuclear war.

For 'Interpreting the Cold War', ask for feedback from the students on each interpretation. They may need additional assistance in putting together their own, balanced interpretation. Students should concentrate on key factors, such as Soviet expansion into eastern Europe and the US use of the atomic bomb.

For 'Interpreting the Cuban Missile Crisis', complete one example of matching the interpretation to the source as a whole-class activity.

Assessment sheet

Students should complete this sheet to evaluate their overall understanding of the Cold War and of the key skills developed.

Plenary

Review the Cold War with questions such as: Whose interpretation do you more readily accept – US or Soviet and why? Why do you think the Cuban Missile Crisis did not lead to nuclear war? Which side do you think got most from the crisis?

The reasons for the Cold War

In the years following 1945, a Cold War developed between the two superpowers, the USA and the Soviet Union.

Western interpretations

The Western interpretation was that given by the USA and the countries of western Europe. These countries believed in democracy where people are free to vote for the rulers .

Such countries feared the spread of communism as it would threaten democracy. They were particularly worried by Soviet expansion into the countries of eastern Europe, especially as these countries were not allowed free elections and were more or less forced to accept communist governments. These states were controlled by the Soviet Union. They feared that Soviet communism would soon spread to western Europe.

The USA used atomic bombs on Japan to end the war in the Far East quickly.

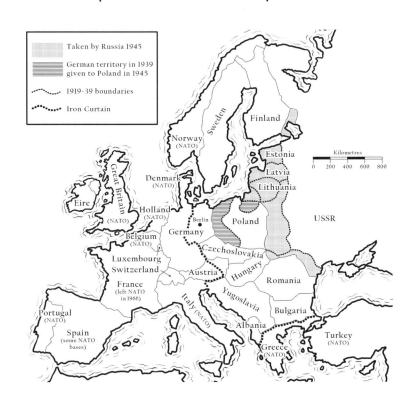

Soviet interpretations

The Soviet Union had twice been invaded by Germany, once in 1914 and again in 1941.

Stalin insisted that the countries in eastern Europe were controlled to protect the Soviet Union from future invasion – security. In other words, he wanted them to act as a buffer. He also insisted that the communist system was better than the democratic system of the West. Communism believes that all people are equal and that they cannot be really free until they are equal. Otherwise freedom is only for the rich.

Stalin also insisted that the USA used the atomic bomb as a warning to the Soviet Union and should have consulted him first.

The Cuban Missile Crisis

December 1961 Castro declares Cuba, only 150 kilometres from the US mainland, a communist country. He asks the Soviet Union to provide arms to defend Cuba from a possible US invasion.

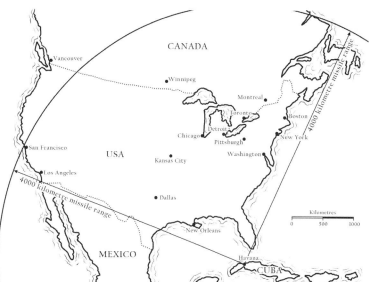

Beginning September 1962 Khrushchev, the Soviet leader, starts to send nuclear weapons to Cuba.

4 September Kennedy, the US president, warns the Soviet Union not to put nuclear missiles on Cuba.

14 October A US spy plane takes a series of photographs 12 miles above the island which showed medium-range ballistic missiles.

16 October Kennedy has a meeting of his top advisers to decide what to do. Should they use nuclear weapons against Cuba or even attack the Soviet Union?

22 October Kennedy announces a naval blockade of Cuba. All ships carrying weapons to and from Cuba are to be searched.

23 October Khrushchev insists that the Soviet Union is simply helping Cuba to defend itself and accuses the USA of pushing the world towards nuclear war.

24 October Twenty-five Soviet ships reach the blockade. All turn back except an oil tanker that is allowed to pass through unsearched.

26 October Khrushchev sends a letter to Kennedy offering a way out of the crisis. The Soviet Union will remove its missiles from Cuba if the USA removes its from Turkey.

27 October Kennedy's brother, Robert, makes a deal with Khrushchev over Cuba and Turkey but insists that the removal of US missiles from Turkey should be kept secret.

28 October Radio Moscow announces that the nuclear weapons will be removed from Cuba.

Interpreting the Cold War

☞ Here are two interpretations of the reasons for the Cold War. Read them both, then answer the questions below.

Interpretation A	Interpretation B
We had no option but to expand into eastern Europe and set up communist governments. We had to think of our future security. After all, in two world wars we had been invaded by Germany with enormous damage to our country and millions of deaths. We need a buffer to prevent another such invasion. In any case, our rival has developed and used the atom bomb without telling us.	There is no excuse for taking over these countries of eastern Europe. They have not been allowed free elections but forced to accept this system of government. This is the first stage to further expansion in western Europe which we need to stop. We have to protect democracy. We only used the atom bomb to end the war in the Far East and not as a threat.

Give two differences between the two interpretations.

1._____

2._____

☞ Write a balanced interpretation of the reasons for the Cold War which does not favour either side. On a separate sheet of paper, copy and complete the writing frame below.

> The Cold War was due to …
>
> On the one side, the USA …
>
> On the other side, the Soviet Union …
>
> Overall, the most important reason was …
>
> This was because …

Activity sheet – The Cold War

Interpreting the Cuban Missile Crisis

☞ Below are interpretations of some of the Cuban Missile Crisis. Complete the table by matching the interpretations to the sources. Some interpretations might match more than one source.

Interpretation	Source or sources
The Cuban Missile Crisis could have led to nuclear war.	
The Soviet Union was right to defend Cuba.	
The USA had no choice but to act against Cuba.	
The Cuban Missile Crisis was a defeat for the USA.	
Kennedy acted decisively against the Soviet Union.	
The Cuban Missile Crisis was a defeat for Khrushchev.	
The Cuban Missile Crisis was a victory for Khrushchev.	

We had an obligation to do everything in our power to protect Cuba's existence as a communist country and as a working example to every other country in Latin America.
Source A Extract from Khrushchev's memoirs

I have unmistakeable evidence that a series of offensive missile sites are now in preparation. To halt this offensive build-up, a strict blockade on all military equipment under shipment to Cuba is being introduced.
Source B Part of a broadcast by President Kennedy

Army General: 'We'd given Castro too much and let him off too easily'. Admiral: 'We've been had'. Air Force General: 'It is the greatest defeat in our history, Mr President.'
Source C The verdict of top US commanders

Khrushchev claimed that he had achieved the aim of preventing a US invasion of Cuba. He was, however, criticised by China for backing down in the face of US threats.
Source D From a modern world textbook

I remember going into a cinema the next evening and wondering 'will I walk out again?'
Source E A young woman recalls the crisis

Assessment sheet – The Cold War

✓ Tick the boxes to show what you know.

I know:

	Yes	Not sure	Don't know
who the superpowers were in 1945			
who first used the atomic bomb			
what the Soviet interpretation of the Cold War was			
what the Western interpretation of the Cold War was			
why there was a crisis over Cuba in 1962			
why it did not lead to a nuclear war			
how to write my own interpretation			

I know best: _____

I need to work on (up to three targets):

—

—

—

Teacher's notes

Votes for women

Objectives

- Understand different methods used to get the vote
- Problem solve and make decisions

Prior knowledge

Students should have some understanding of the position of women in Britain at the beginning of the twentieth century.

QCA link

Unit 16 The franchise: why did it take so much longer for British women to get the vote?

NC links

History skills 2a, 2c, 2e, 5a, 5b and 5c

Scottish attainment targets

Environmental Studies – Society – People in the past
Strand – Change, continuity, cause and effect
Level D
Strand – People, events and societies of significance in the past
Level E

Background

Women in 1900 were second-class citizens who were seen but not heard. They had the traditional role of getting married, having children and running the household. Their education was limited to subjects useful to fulfilling this role. Working married women had limited employment opportunities, more especially poorly paid unskilled work in cotton mills, sweated trades and domestic service. Wealthier married women were not expected to work. Those who did not marry could be teachers, governesses, nurses or office workers.

Starter activity

Ask the students whether women in Britain have the vote today. If so, at what age? Explain that in 1900, women did not have the vote in general elections. Ask them to suggest possible reasons why they did not have the vote.

Resource sheets and activity sheets

Divide students into groups with each group researching one of the three societies on 'The campaign for the vote, 1900–14' and 'The suffragettes'. Obtain feedback through role plays that illustrate the different methods of each society.

For 'The three women's societies', students should not have any difficulty matching the three figures to the methods. The second activity could be preceded by a whole-class discussion on the achievements and shortcomings of each society. Encourage volunteers to read out their final judgement.

For 'Hunger striking and force-feeding', the student should work in groups to discuss each option and reach a final group decision. Use the feedback from each group to lead to a whole-class discussion.

Assessment sheet

Students should complete this sheet to evaluate their overall understanding of the votes for women and of the key skills developed.

Plenary

Ask the students whether the suffragettes did more harm than good and follow this with a class vote on the question.

The campaign for the vote, 1900–14

In 1900, women in Britain did not have the vote in national elections. Women were thought to be less intelligent than men and too emotional to be involved in politics.

Societies for the vote

Three different societies campaigned for the vote – two of these are described below.

The NUWSS

The National Union of Women's Suffrage Societies was set up in 1898 by Millicent Fawcett to campaign for suffrage (which means the right to vote). They believed that women would get the vote eventually. All they had to do was to keep on the right side of the law, and do all they could to persuade the general public and parliament that women ought to be given the vote.

They organised marches and petitions and used peaceful methods that showed that women were sensible enough to deserve the vote. They were known as suffragists. However, their methods did take a lot of time to get results.

Source A A peaceful march through London in 1913 ▶

The WFL

The Women's Freedom League was set up in 1909 by Charlotte Despard. Charlotte had been a Women's Social and Political Union (WSPU) member but felt the society was becoming too violent in its methods. She left the WSPU and set up the WFL, which was prepared to break the law but not in a violent manner. Here are some of their methods:

- They refused to take part in the census of 1911, the official population count, by not filling in the census form.
- Others chained themselves to the railings outside the House of Commons and picketed the members.
- They refused to pay taxes arguing that they were not represented in parliament.

The suffragettes

The WSPU

The third, and possibly most famous of the societies, was the Women's Social and Political Union set up by Emmeline Pankhurst and her daughters, Sylvia and Christabel, in Manchester in 1903.

They used more militant or extreme methods in an effort to get publicity and force the government to give them the vote. They were often arrested.

- They broke up political meetings and assaulted leading members of the Liberal government.

- In 1912, they smashed hundreds of shop windows, starting in the expensive streets of London. A total of 219 suffragettes were arrested.

- They slashed paintings and poured acid into post boxes and on the greens of golf courses because many leading Liberals played golf. They also set fire to derelict buildings.

Force-feeding

When the suffragettes were sent to prison many women went on hunger strike to get publicity for their cause. The prison authorities were frightened that a suffragette might die in prison. This could give them even more publicity and make them martyrs. So the prison authorities began force-feeding prisoners. Prison officers pushed a tube down the throat and into the stomach. They then poured liquid food down the tube.

Force-feeding brought bad publicity for the Liberal government. In 1913, they introduced the Temporary Discharge Act. This was nicknamed the 'Cat and Mouse Act'. Prisoners on hunger strike were released when very ill and sent back to prison when they were better. This was like a cat that frequently catches and releases a mouse before killing it.

The three women's societies

☞ Below is a member of each of the women's societies. Draw a line from each society member to match them to their correct speech.

> The only way to get the vote is by being militant. We need to make a nuisance of ourselves by assaulting members of the government and, when arrested, going on hunger strikes.

> We have to prove to men that we can act responsibly and deserve the vote. We must organise meetings, marches and petitions. We must act in a sensible and peaceful manner.

> I reject violence. However, we may have to break the law to get the vote. We must refuse to pay taxes, or to take part in the 1911 census. We could chain ourselves to the railings outside the House of Commons.

☞ Decide which of the three societies you think did most to further votes for women. Then, place each society somewhere on the rating line below and give a brief explanation for each decision.

| Nothing | Very little | Quite a lot | A lot |

Now fully explain your decision.

I believe that _____ did most to further votes for women.

This is because _____

_____

Activity sheet – Votes for women

Hunger striking and force-feeding

☞ Your group are the key members of the Liberal government in the year 1913. You have a major problem to solve.

The problem: Members of the militant suffragettes are being arrested.

Possible solutions: The table below shows your possible options. Complete the table by:

- writing the advantages/disadvantages of each option
- rating each option out of 5 (5 = very good option, down to 1 = very poor).

Option	Advantages	Disadvantages	Rating 1–5
Not arrest the suffragettes			
If they hunger strike, allow them to die			
If they hunger strike, force-feed them			
Temporary Discharge Act			

☞ Now make your final judgement. On a separate sheet of paper, copy and complete the writing frame below.

> We have decided on the following option…
>
> This is because…
>
> We have rejected the option…
>
> because…
>
> Furthermore, we have rejected the option…
>
> because…
>
> Finally, we have rejected the option…
>
> because…

☞ Prepare a one-minute presentation to the class to explain why your group have chosen this option and rejected the others.

Assessment sheet – Votes for women

✓ Tick the boxes to show what you know.

I know:

	Yes	Not sure	Don't know
what is meant by a suffragette			
what is meant by a suffragist			
why some suffragettes went on hunger strike			
why some suffragettes were force-fed			
who was leader of the suffragettes			
what is meant by the WFL			
how to rank order factors			

I know best: _____

I need to work on (up to three targets):

–

–

–

Teacher's notes

A divided Ireland

Objectives

- Understand the background to the recent 'troubles' in Ireland
- Organise and link events chronologically
- Use a Venn diagram

Prior knowledge

Students should be able to use a Venn diagram and have some understanding of the geographical and political position of Ireland.

QCA link

Unit 17 Divided Ireland: why has it been so hard to achieve peace in Ireland?

NC links

History skills 1, 2b, 2c, 2e, 5a and 5c

Scottish attainment targets

Environmental Studies – Society – People in the past
Strand – Time and historical sequence
Level C
Strand – Change, continuity, cause and effect
Level E

Background

Ireland, although a geographical entity, is separated politically. Southern Ireland, predominantly Catholic, is a republic; while Northern Ireland remains part of the UK and has a protestant majority, although there is a significant Catholic minority.

Starter activity

Using Source A on 'The Recent "troubles"', ask the students to describe what is happening in as much detail as possible. For example, they have to imagine they are describing the scene to someone who cannot see the illustration. This could then lead to questions such 'Why is this happening?' and 'Who is to blame?'.

Resource sheets and activity sheets

For 'Key events in Irish history, 1600–1968', set the scene by explaining that the problems of Ireland date back over several hundred years.

Use 'The recent "troubles"' to explain the key events.

For 'Why is Ireland divided?', show the students the example provided and complete another example as a whole-class activity. Ask students to organise the statements on 'Key events in Irish history, 1600–1968' in chronological order and write in a link between each event.

For 'Who was most to blame?', explain how to use a Venn diagram and ask the students to work in pairs. Obtain feedback from the students and plot the statements on a master diagram.

Assessment sheet

Students should complete this sheet to evaluate their overall understanding of a divided Ireland and of the key skills developed.

Plenary

Ask the students what they would do if they could change the past. What would they do to prevent the long-term problems on 'Why is Ireland divided?' How might they have prevented the recent 'troubles'? Also pose the question: Was religion the fundamental cause of the 'troubles'?

Key events in Irish history, 1600–1968

In 1690, William of Orange defeated a Catholic army led by James II at the Battle of the Boyne. William encouraged more protestant settlers in Ulster to set up the linen industry. Catholic–Protestant rivalry continued.

In 1916, the Catholic Irish Republican Brotherhood (later IRA) carried out the Easter Uprising. The rebellion failed and the British executed many of the leaders who then became martyrs. This increased support for Sinn Fein, a party which favours a republic.

Oliver Cromwell wanted to crush the Catholics in Ireland. In 1649, he sent an army which massacred many Catholics in Drogheda. This increased the Catholics' hatred for the British.

In 1921, Ireland was partitioned. The mainly Protestant Ulster, in the north, remained part of the United Kingdom and the mainly Catholic south eventually became a republic.

In 1798, Irish Catholics rebelled against British rule. The rebellion was crushed with 560 Irish rebels executed and 70 transported.

In 1607, James I sent Protestants who became large landowners. They were resented by the Catholics.

In 1912, the British Prime Minister, Asquith, tried to introduce home rule for Ireland. This was opposed by many Protestant Unionists in Ulster as it would lead to a Catholic controlled government and they wanted to keep the union with Britain. The First World War prevented home rule.

In 1800, the Act of Union meant that Ireland lost its parliament and was ruled directly by the British parliament. Catholics could not vote or be members of parliament.

In 1922–68, Ulster was ruled by a Protestant majority who ensured that all the best housing, jobs and schools went to protestants. The Catholics felt like second-class citizens. The IRA continues to campaign for a united Ireland – Ulster joined with the south.

In 1641, the Catholics rebelled and massacred 3000 Protestant settlers.

Resource sheet – A divided Ireland

The recent 'troubles'

From 1968, Ireland, especially Ulster, suffered a series of troubles. The Catholics of Ulster began campaigning for civil or equal rights. This led to violent clashes with the many Protestants.

Source A Police and Catholics clash

1 The Protestant Unionists in Northern Ireland chose not to share government with the Catholics, who were discriminated against in education, housing and employment.

2 In 1967, Catholics in Northern Ireland set up the Northern Ireland Civil Rights Association (NICRA). It wanted an end to all discrimination and equal rights for Catholics.

3 Protestant Unionist extremists led by Ian Paisley refused to give civil rights to Catholics.

4 NICRA organised marches to get publicity for their movement. One such march was through the Protestant area of Londonderry on 5 October 1968. The British authorities, fearing trouble, banned the march but it still went ahead.

5 During the march, the marchers clashed with the mainly Protestant police and many Catholics were badly injured as the police used batons against the marchers.

6 In 1969, British troops were sent into the streets of Belfast and Londonderry to end the violence.

7 The IRA stepped up their campaign for a united Ireland and used terrorist methods against the police and army.

8 The British government introduced internment or imprisonment of suspected terrorists without trail.

9 In 1974, the British government brought in a 15-member power-sharing government of Catholics and Protestants. Protestant extremists destroyed it by organising a general strike.

10 In 1982, elections for a Northern Ireland Assembly took place. There was little support for this from the IRA and Protestant extremists. It was abolished in 1986.

11 In 1994, the IRA agreed to a ceasefire and began talks with the British government. Two years later, the IRA ended the peace talks by exploding a bomb in London.

12 In 1998, talks between the Catholics, the Protestants and the British government lead to the Good Friday Agreement. The majority of voters in Northern Ireland and the Irish Republic supported the agreement. However, the IRA exploded another bomb at Omagh killing 29 people.

Why is Ireland divided?

☞ Create a flow chart to show the key events from 1600–1968. Do this by:

- using the events shown on resource sheet 'Key events in Irish history, 1600–1968' and arranging them in chronological order.

- writing a link between each event to show how the effects of one event led to the next.

Continue on a separate sheet of paper if needed. The first one has been done for you.

1607   James I sent Protestants who became large landowners. They were resented by the Catholics.

(In the above event, James I upset the Catholics by his actions. This led to the Catholic rebellion mentioned in the next event.)

1641   The Catholics rebelled and massacred 3000 Protestant settlers.

Who was most to blame?

☞ The resource sheet 'The recent "troubles"' shows a series of statements about Ireland from 1968–2000.

Place the statement numbers on the Venn diagram to show which of the following was most to blame for preventing a solution to the problems of Ireland:

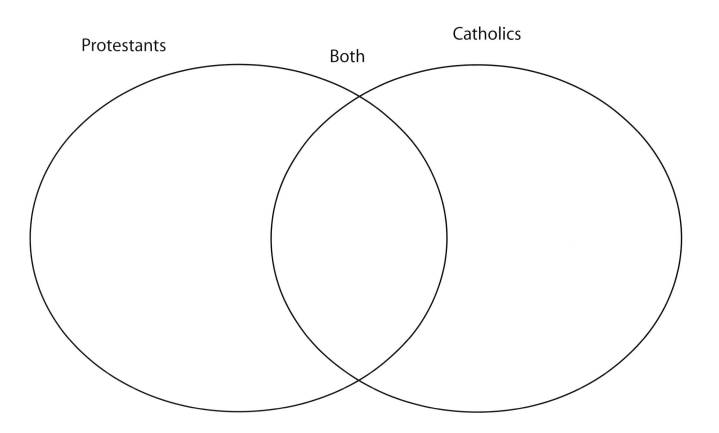

Protestants   Both   Catholics

☞ Who has been most to blame for the delay in finding a solution? Write your answer below.

I think that most to blame has been _____

This is because _____

_____

Assessment sheet – A divided Ireland

✓ Tick the boxes that show what you know.

I know:

	Yes	Not sure	Don't know
why Cromwell is hated by Irish Catholics			
what is meant by the Act of Union			
how Ireland became divided in 1921			
what is meant by Ulster			
what methods were used by the IRA			
what the Good Friday Agreement is			
how to use a Venn diagram			
how to organise events chronologically			

I know best: _____

I need to work on (up to three targets):

–

–

–

Teacher's notes

Persecution of the Jews in Germany, 1933–39

Objectives

- Understand the persecution of the Jews in Germany, 1933–39
- Empathise with the Jews

Prior knowledge

Students should be able to emphasise and write entries in a diary.

QCA link

Unit 19 How and why did the Holocaust happen?

NC links

History skills 1, 2a, 2b, 2c, 2e, 5a, 5b and 5c

Scottish attainment targets

Environmental Studies – Society – People in the past
Strand – Change, continuity, cause and effect
Level E

Background

Anti-Semitism is not new. It goes back to the early Middle Ages when Jews were systematically persecuted. They were blamed for the death of Christ and were often used as a scapegoat for any disasters. Hitler spent several years in Vienna where there was strong anti-Semitism. In the inter-war years, many Germans were looking for a scapegoat for Germany's defeat in the First World War and subsequent humiliation. Hitler provided such a scapegoat in the shape of the Jews.

Starter activity

Ask the students to read the two extracts from the diary of Anne Frank on 'Diary of a Jew in Germany, 1933–39'. What do they know about her? In pairs, students should find out about her by using the Internet or other resources. They should have focused questions, such as: Who was she? What age was she when she wrote the diary? What eventually happened to her?

Resource sheets and activity sheets

Ask the students to study the persecution of the Jews on 'The Jews in Nazi Germany, 1933–39' and consider these questions: Why was the persecution gradually increased rather than introduced immediately? Which do they think were the worst measures?

For the 'Diary of a Jew in Germany, 1933–39', stress to the students that they need to make their diary entries based on the key measures introduced by the Nazis. How would they feel? Why would the measures make life more unpleasant? Entries should be three or four sentences long. Encourage students to share their entries with the whole class.

Assessment sheet

Students should complete this sheet to evaluate their overall understanding of the persecution of the Jews in Germany and of the key skills developed.

Plenary

Many Jews remained in Germany. Discuss why with the class. Answers could include: they lived there for generations and had all their belongings, friends and family; other countries would not take them. What would the students have done? Would they have remained and put up with the persecution. If they did leave, at what stage would the persecution have become intolerable?

The Jews in Nazi Germany, 1933–39

In January 1933, Hitler became Chancellor of Germany and began a campaign of persecuting the Jews. The position of Jews in Germany gradually got worse during the years 1933–39.

1933

- Hitler ordered a boycott of Jewish shops and businesses.
- Thousands of Jewish civil servants, lawyers and university teachers were sacked.

1934

- Local councils banned Jews from public places such as parks, playing fields and swimming pools.

1935

- The Nuremberg Laws were passed. Jews were denied German citizenship and lost the right to vote and hold government office.
- The Law for the Protection of German Blood and Honour forbade marriage or sexual relations between Jews and German citizens.

1936

- Jews were banned from being vets, dentists, accountants, surveyors, teachers and nurses.
- Jews were often singled out at schools by teachers and bullied by other students.

1937

- Hitler made a strong speech attacking Jews.

1938

- A German diplomat was murdered by a Jew in Paris. The Nazis encouraged Kristallnacht or 'Crystal Night', 9 November – a two-day campaign during which Jewish shops, homes and synagogues were destroyed. Ninety Jews were killed and 20 000 arrested.
- Jews with non-Jewish first names had to add and use the name 'Israel' for males and 'Sarah' for females.

1939

- Jews were no longer allowed to run shops or businesses.
- They had to pay a huge fine for the damage caused by Kristallnacht.

Diary of a Jew in Germany, 1933–39

Anne Frank was Jewish and became famous because she wrote a diary of her years in hiding in Nazi-occupied Holland before her family was captured in 1944. Here are two extracts from her diary.

9 October 1942	**19 November 1942**
Our Jewish friends are being taken away by the dozen. It is impossible to escape. Most of the people in the camp in Holland are branded as inmates by their shaven heads. If it is as bad as this in Holland, whatever will it be like in the barbarous regions they are sent to? The British radio speaks of their being gassed.	Evening after evening the grey and green lorries trundle past. The Germans ring at every door to enquire if there are Jews living in the house. If they are, then the whole family has to go at once. If they don't find any, they go into the next house. No one has a chance of evading them unless they are hiding.

 Imagine you are a Jewish teenager living in Germany from 1933 to 1939 and you keep your own diary. Write your reactions to the changes brought by the Nazis explained on 'The Jews in Nazi Germany, 1933–39'. Below are two pages for your diary. Create at least two other diary entries on a separate sheet of paper.

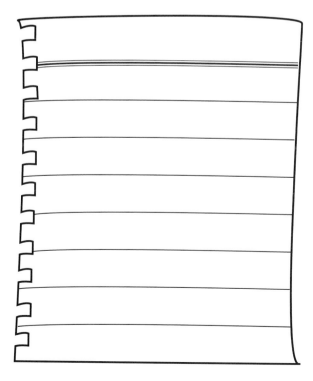

Assessment sheet – Persecution of the Jews in Germany, 1933–39

✓ Tick the boxes that show what you know.

I know:

	Yes	Not sure	Don't know
what happened to Jewish shops in 1933			
how many Jews lost their jobs			
what is meant by the Nuremberg Laws			
what happened on Kristallnacht			
why some Jews had to change their first names			
why many Jews tried to leave Germany			
how to write diary entries			

I know best: _____

I need to work on (up to three targets):

–

–

–

Teacher's notes

The Final Solution

Objectives

- Understand the horrors of the Final Solution
- Make inferences from sources
- Use a mind map to summarise key features

Prior knowledge

Students should be able to use mind maps.

QCA link

Unit 19 How and why did the Holocaust happen?

NC links

History skills 2a, 2c, 5a, 5b and 5c

Scottish attainment targets

Environmental Studies – Society – People in the past
Strand – Change, continuity, cause and effect
Level E

Background

German armies were very successful in the first three years of the Second World War and, by 1942, had occupied huge areas of eastern Europe. However, this included millions of Jews under Nazi control. Initially, they were herded into ghettos. In 1942, Hitler met with other leading Nazis at the Wannsee Conference. Here the decision was taken to carry out the Final Solution. At first this was done by SS murder squads until a more efficient method, the gas chambers, was developed for the mass murder of the Jews.

Starter activity

Students need to understand the early Nazi successes in the Second World War. Using an appropriate map, ask the students to write down, in chronological order, the areas/countries occupied by the Nazis between 1939 and 1941. Why do they think this would increase the Jewish problem for Hitler? What solutions did he have? Tease out the possibility of ghettos, deportation and mass murder.

Resource sheets and activity sheets

Students should read 'What was the Final Solution?' and make notes on the key features using the five 'W's – where, when, who, what and how.

For 'Final Solution mind map', students may need further guidance to complete their mind map. Complete one more 'branch' as a whole-class exercise. Once completed, build a whole-class mind map with information from the students' maps. Ask the students how useful mind maps are for summarising key features. In pairs, ask students to write down the uses of mind mapping for other topics in history and in other subject areas. Encourage feedback from each pair. Brainstorm with students on reasons why they think it is important to remember the Holocaust.

Assessment sheet

Students should complete this sheet to evaluate their overall understanding of the Final Solution and of the key skills developed.

Plenary

Ask the students: Could the Holocaust have been prevented? If so, when and how? Why is it important to remember the Holocaust?

What was the Final Solution?

The Final Solution

No one is certain when Hitler decided on the 'Final Solution' or the extermination of the Jews. Top Nazi leaders did have a conference in 1942 where they discussed the problem of the Jews. This was probably when the decision was taken. The Jewish problem greatly increased as German armies conquered more and more of eastern Europe in the years 1939 to 1942. Millions of Jews now came under Nazi occupation.

Carrying it out

At first, Jews were killed by SS murder squads known as the Einsatzgruppen. Here an SS soldier describes what happened:

We go into the wood and find a spot suitable for mass executions. We order the prisoners to dig their graves. The two women go first to be shot. The shooting goes on. Nearly all fall into the grave unconscious.

However, this was time-consuming, wasted bullets, and was sometimes distressing for those watching.

Slave labour

A more efficient method was needed. Jews were transported in crowded trains to extermination camps, such as Auschwitz and Belsen, in the East, especially Poland. On arrival, selection took place. The fit were taken as slave labour. They were treated with great brutality. Conditions were terrible. Food was scarce as the Nazis deliberately starved them to death.

The gas chambers

The old, very young, sick and pregnant mothers were usually taken immediately to be executed in the gas chambers. The new arrivals believed they were being sent for a shower as the gas rooms were camouflaged as shower rooms with pipes, dressing rooms and clothes hooks.

The prisoners stripped off and assembled in the gas chambers. Carbon monoxide or Zyclon B was then used to kill the assembled prisoners. The aim was to operate the Final Solution as efficiently as possible. As many as five million Jews were killed in the extermination camps from 1942 to 1945.

Activity sheet – The Final Solution

Final Solution mind map

☞ Using the mind map below, summarise the main features of the Final Solution.

- Write 'The Final Solution' in the central box.
- For the surrounding boxes, use the five 'W's – Why, what, where, when, who together with 'how'. One box has been done for you.

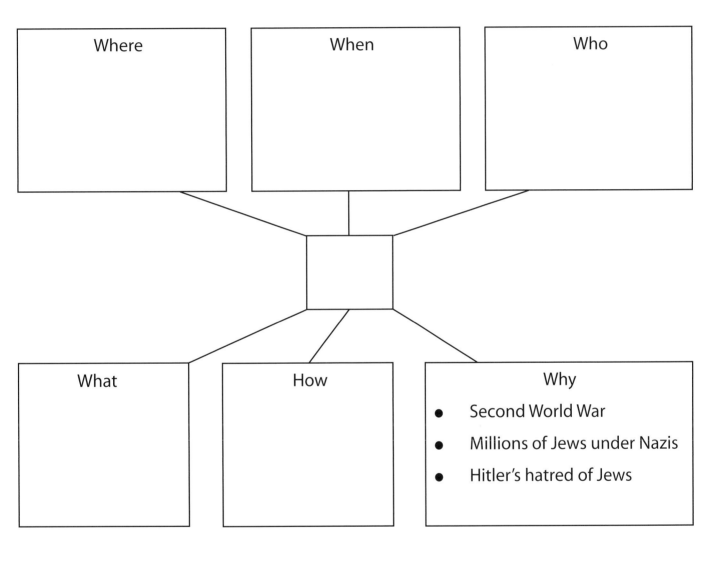

Where	When	Who

What	How	Why

Why
- Second World War
- Millions of Jews under Nazis
- Hitler's hatred of Jews

☞ One survivor of the death camps wrote his account and called it 'A Spectator in Hell'. Why is this a very appropriate title?

This is a very appropriate title because _____

_____

Assessment sheet – The Final Solution

Specials!

✓ Tick the boxes that show what you know.

I know:

	Yes	Not sure	Don't know
what is meant by the Final Solution			
who the Einstatzgruppen were			
what happened to the healthy Jews at the death camps of Belsen			
what happened to the old, very young and unfit			
how the Final Solution was carried out			
why those who discovered these camps were horrified			
how to use a mind map			

I know best: _____

I need to work on (up to three targets):

—

—

—

Teacher's notes

Twentieth-century medicine

Objectives

- Understand key developments in medicine in the twentieth century
- Make judgements on the importance of individuals and the NHS
- Use sources in enquiry

Prior knowledge

Students should be able to interpret sources.

QCA link

Unit 20 Twentieth-century medicine: how has it changed the lives of people?

NC links

History skills 2c, 2e, 4a, 4b, 5a, 5b and 5c

Scottish attainment targets

Environmental Studies – Society – People in the past
Strand – Change, continuity, cause and effect
Level E

Background

At the beginning of the twentieth century, there was no NHS in Britain and many people died from lack of treatment and knowledge. The greatest problem was poverty and the cost of seeing a doctor or having hospital treatment. While Joseph Lister had greatly improved hygiene in hospitals and surgery, there was, as yet, no man-made drug that could deal with infection. This was highlighted by the numerous casualties during the First World War.

Starter activity

Ask students to write down a definition of the National Health Service in less than 50 words. Obtain feedback from the students and try to come up with a whole-class definition. Brainstorm with the students about the various services provided by the NHS.

Resource sheet and activity sheet

For 'The discovery of penicillin', divide the class with one half researching Fleming and the other half researching Florey and Chain. Each half should then give feedback on their results.

For 'The National Health Service', use one source as a whole-class exercise and/or divide the students into groups with each group researching a source and giving feedback to the whole class.

For 'Pioneers of medicine', arrange students in groups to research and summarise the importance of one medical discovery.

For 'Who discovered penicillin?', stress to the students that there is no right or wrong answer and that they can opt for both suspects. However, they need to justify their decision. This could prompt a whole-class discussion and even a vote.

For 'The NHS: has it been a success?', students should classify the sources in the grid. Stress that some sources may go in both columns. Once the grid is completed, encourage a balanced judgement. Again, stress that there is no right or wrong answer. Students could use a software package for the layout of the article. This could lead to a whole-class discussion on the NHS.

For 'Who's who in twentieth-century medicine', students should make an informed judgement. Ask for feedback from the students on their rank order. Explain that they need to justify their top choice.

Assessment sheet

Students should complete this sheet to evaluate their overall understanding of twentieth-century medicine and of the key skills developed.

Plenary

Students should be asked about the future of the NHS: Should it be kept? Is it better to encourage private medicine and medical insurance? If kept, what improvements should be made to the NHS?

The discovery of penicillin

The development of antibiotics has been vital for the treatment of infections. The earliest and most important was penicillin, which is made from a mould called penicillin. Who discovered it?

Alexander Fleming

Fleming worked as a doctor during the First World War and saw that, despite sterilisation, gangrene and blood poisoning were common in wounds caused by shrapnel and bullets. After the war, he carried out experiments to find a chemical to deal with the main germ found in wounds, staphylococci. He left dirty dishes lying about for a long time and in 1928 made a chance discovery – on one of the dishes was a mould.

On investigation, he found that penicillin had got into the dish, possibly blown through an open window. Fleming now realised that penicillin could be applied to, or injected into, areas infected with penicillin-sensitive microbes. In 1929, he wrote an article in which he explained his discovery.

Unfortunately Fleming was unable to repeat the experiment. He did not have the facilities or money to develop and test his idea that penicillin could be used to fight infection. His discovery was virtually ignored and he went back to his old work.

Florey and Chain

In the 1930s, two Oxford scientists, Howard Florey and Ernst Chain, became interested in Fleming's article on penicillin. In 1939, they gathered together a skilled team of scientists and got money from the British government to fund further research. They were able to:

- grow the penicillin using a combination of the latest freeze-drying technology and some more traditional equipment. They grew the bacteria in thousands of milk bottles.

- test the penicillin on eight mice. They were all injected with dangerous germs. Four mice were then given penicillin. Four were not. The four who had been given penicillin lived and the other four died.

By 1941, they had grown enough penicillin to use on a human patient. It worked at first but they could not produce enough penicillin and the patient died.

In the following year, the British and US governments agreed to jointly fund the mass production of the drug. By 1944, enough was being produced to treat all the Allied wounded.

The National Health Service

In 1946, the Labour government agreed to set up a National Health Service (NHS). It was officially launched in 1948 to provide medical services for everyone, free of charge and paid for by the state.

The NHS threatens the freedom and independence of doctors and patients. Doctors will become government servants.

Source A From a newspaper, February 1946

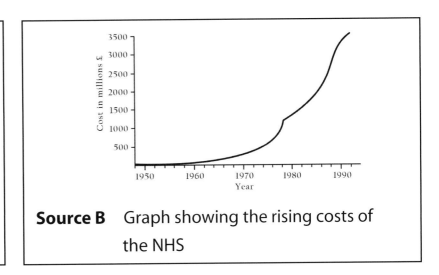

Source B Graph showing the rising costs of the NHS

Mother went and got tested for new glasses. Then she went further down the road for the chiropodist. She had her feet done. She went back to the doctor's because she was having trouble with her ears. The doctor said he would fix her up with a hearing aid.

Source C Alice Law recalling 5 July 1948, the first day of the National Health Service

The NHS has made women's health a priority and has continued to do so. Women are now four times more likely to consult a doctor than a man. Life expectancy for women has risen from 66 to 78 since 1948.

Source D From a history of medicine published in 1996

The standard of cleanliness in NHS wards and corridors has declined because of reduced spending. This means that hospitals are not as infection-free as before. There has been a shortage of beds for patients or facilities for intensive care. Operations are often cancelled or patients with life-threatening conditions moved.

Source E From a history of medicine published in 1997

Pioneers of medicine

Paul Erlich

In 1909, Paul Erlich developed the first 'magic-bullet' – a chemical drug that was man-made and would work inside a person's body, killing germs that were causing infectious illnesses. It was called Salvarsan 606. It killed the germ that caused the disease syphilis, without harming the rest of the person's body. Syphilis killed thousands of people at that time. Not all doctors used the new drug because it was not soluble and was painful to inject into people's veins.

Alexander Fleming

He accidentally discovered penicillin. Refer to 'The discovery of penicillin'.

Gerhard Domagk

In 1932, Domagk discovered a second magic bullet. He tried Prontonsil, a red dye, on mice. The results were good. It seemed to stop bacteria from multiplying in the mice. He then got the opportunity to test Prontonsil on a human much sooner than expected. His daughter pricked her finger and developed severe blood poisoning. With his daughter near to death, Domagk risked using Prontonsil and she recovered. By 1938, it was being produced commercially. However, it sometimes damages a person's liver and kidneys.

Howard Florey and Ernst Chain

They further developed penicillin. Refer to 'The discovery of penicillin'.

Francis Crick and James Watson

Deoxyribonucleic acid, better known as DNA, stores genetic code and is the key to a person's genetic make-up. Two scientists, Francis Crick and James Watson, discovered the structure of DNA in 1953. They showed that a person's genetic code is organised in a double structure, which consists of a pair of interlocking spirals joined together by a pair of molecules. This discovery has meant that medical conditions such as cystic fibrosis can be detected and treated earlier. It has greatly helped the police in detecting criminals. However, it has also led to the controversial cloning of animals and plants.

Who discovered penicillin?

☞ Imagine you are a detective who has been asked to solve the following medical mystery.

The mystery: who invented penicillin?

The suspects

Suspect 1   *Alexander Fleming*

Suspects 2   *Howard Florey and Ernst Chain*

The evidence: use the evidence from 'The discovery of pencillin' to complete the grid below.

The suspects	For discovery	Against discovery
Fleming		
Florey and Chain		

Your verdict

I believe that _____ was/were responsible for the development of

penicillin because _____

_____

The other _____ was/were not as responsible

because _____

_____

The NHS: has it been a success?

☞ It is 1998 and the fiftieth anniversary of the launch of the National Health Service. You are a journalist on a national newspaper and have been asked to research and write an article with the title 'Has the National Health Service been a success?'

1 Organise the sources on the NHS from 'The National Health Service' into the categories below.

Successes	Failures

2 Write the article. Copy and complete the frame below.

- You will need a catchy headline.
- Ensure the article is balanced by giving successes and failures.
- Use 'The National Health Service' for sources – you should give people's views.
- You will need to come to a final judgement on the original question.
- You could use a relevant software package to create the article.

Name of newspaper		Price
	HEADLINE	
Introduction	Illustration	Illustration
Set the scene by exploring when and why the NHS was set up. Explain the purpose of your article.		
Success of the NHS	Failure of the NHS	Final judgement Has it been a success?

Who's who in twentieth-century medicine

☞ You have been asked to compile a 'Who's who' of important pioneers of twentieth-century medicine and to order them from the most important to the least. You have been given a list of names and their achievements but unfortunately the names and achievements have been mixed up.

- Match the achievements to the individual.
- Put them in rank order.
- Explain your choice of first in the rank order.

Fleming	Florey and Chain	Erlich
Domagk	Watson and Crick	

- He accidentally discovered the use of penicillin to attack germs but was unable to fully develop it for use as an antibiotic.
- They discovered the structure of DNA.
- He was able to develop the first magic bullet, called Salvarson 606, which was used in the treatment of syphilis.
- They developed Fleming's work on penicillin and experimented with it using mice and then a human patient.
- He developed the second magic bullet, Protonsil, which was first used on his daughter.

Rank order

	Pioneer	Achievement
1		
2		
3		
4		
5		

Assessment sheet – Twentieth-century medicine

✓ Tick the boxes to show what you know.

I know:

	Yes	Not sure	Don't know
why the discovery of penicillin was so important			
how Fleming discovered penicillin			
how Florey and Chain continued his work			
what is meant by the NHS			
what is meant by DNA			
what was discovered by Erlich			
how to write a newspaper column			

I know best: _____

I need to work on (up to three targets):

 _

 _

 _